Contents

The fold-out geological map

The fold-out geological map can be found in the cover section at the back of this book.

Introduction

Welcome to the landscape of Hadrian's Wall

Hadrian's Wall is known internationally and is a World Heritage Site. The best preserved, and most visited, central sections of the Wall run through some of northern England's most distinctive and striking landscapes. Indeed, it was the remarkable form of this landscape, and the obvious strategic opportunities it presented that influenced the Roman engineers when they designed and sited the Wall. Even without the wealth of Roman remains, this is a beautiful and interesting landscape in its own right and one which rewards exploration.

▼ Looking north-east along the Wall from Housesteads in the evening sunlight. Sewingshields Crags in the distance

Northumberland National Park

Britain's national parks contain some of the nation's finest and most dramatic landscapes. In the far north of England lies Northumberland National Park, the most remote and wild of the English national parks. It stretches from the Cheviot Hills on the Scottish border, to the spectacular central part of Hadrian's Wall in the south. Northumberland National Park is a place of wild and sweeping landscapes, whose character is profoundly influenced by the underlying rocks and landforms. These seemingly wild and natural landscapes are also a product of human activity over many thousands of years.

▲ Milecastle 39 looking east to Crag Lough

What is a World Heritage Site?

World Heritage Sites are places of outstanding cultural and natural importance. Selected by UNESCO (United Nations Educational, Scientific and Cultural Organisation), these sites are recognised as being of global importance and part of the world's heritage. World Heritage status means that sites should be protected, conserved, presented and passed unspoilt to future generations. World Heritage Sites include places as unique and diverse as the Grand Canyon, the Pyramids of Egypt, the Great Barrier Reef and the Great Wall of China. In the United Kingdom there are 26 sites, including the Dorset and East Devon Coast, Stonehenge and Avebury, Durham Castle and Cathedral and Hadrian's Wall.

Why is Hadrian's Wall a World Heritage Site?

In addition to being one of the most iconic archaeological monuments in Britain, Hadrian's Wall is the best preserved and best known frontier of the entire Roman Empire. At the peak of its power the Roman Empire controlled parts of three continents – Europe, Asia and Africa – and was probably the single greatest influence on European civilisation. Nearly 2000 years after its construction, Hadrian's Wall survives as a ruined, but still remarkable, monument to one of the world's great civilisations and the Emperor Hadrian's attempt to 'separate Romans from Barbarians'. It was added to the World Heritage list in 1987.

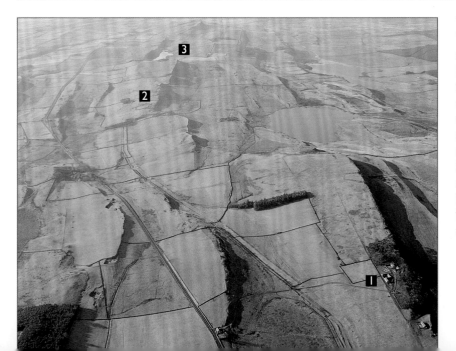

The broad view

The striking pattern of ridges, which epitomises Hadrian's Wall country, is most spectacularly seen from the air. In this view ridges of resistant sandstone and limestone are clearly seen, though most prominent is the scarp of the Whin Sill, which casts dark shadows on its northern side near Sewingshields (1). The Whin Sill crags can be followed westwards towards Housesteads (2) and Crag Lough (3), though their continuity is locally disrupted by several faults.

Beginnings

Solid foundations

The landscape of the Hadrian's Wall area is the result of millions of years of Earth history. Ancient seas and swamps, molten rock, ice, modern rivers, people – all have played their part in the creation of this unique landscape.

A layer-cake of rocks

The very distinctive landscape of this area is made up of layers of sedimentary rocks – limestone, mudstone and sandstone – which were formed as roughly horizontal beds about 325 million years ago.

About 295 million years ago, enormous Earth movements caused the injection of a vast quantity of molten rock from deep within the Earth, into this 'layer-cake' of sedimentary rocks. We see this today as the dolerite of the Whin Sill. These same great Earth movements tilted the rocks so that almost all of them dip to the south.

Limestone, sandstone and especially dolerite are hard and resistant to erosion, and stand out as prominent, often craggy, ridges. Mudstone is soft and weathers rapidly to form the lower ground between the ridges.

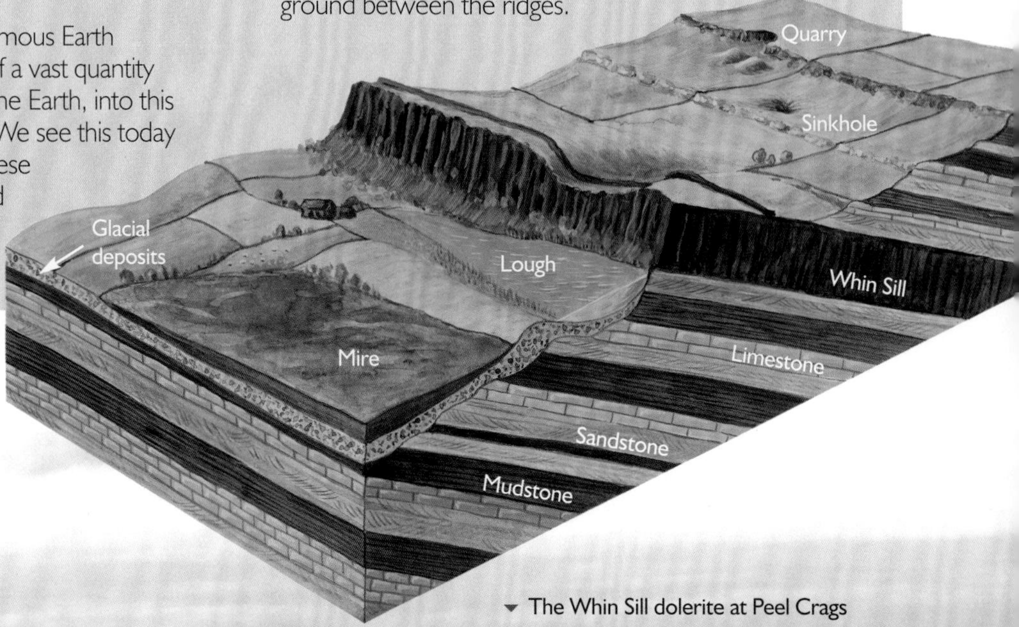

Quarry

Sinkhole

Glacial deposits

Whin Sill

Lough

Limestone

Mire

Sandstone

Mudstone

▼ The Whin Sill dolerite at Peel Crags

Mires

These ancient areas of peat bog date back thousands of years. They started to form when the great wildwood that once clothed the whole of Britain began to recede about 8000 years ago due to a deteriorating climate and the effects of humans.

▼ Hangingshields Rigg Moss

▲ Modern day extraction of limestone and Whin Sill at Barrasford Quarry

Quarries and castles

Through the ages people have used the natural materials in the landscape around them. Sandstone was quarried for building stone, limestone was turned into lime for improving the fields and mineral veins were mined for valuable ores. The Whin Sill is still quarried for aggregate and roadstone.

Loughs

Towards the end of the last ice age, scouring by ice and meltwater flow created water-filled hollows in the lower ground between the ridges. Many became infilled with reeds and bog, but several remain today as small lakes or loughs (pronounced 'loffs'). These relics of the area's glacial past are an important aquatic habitat.

▼ Crag Lough

Glacial deposits

Glacial deposits include debris dumped by huge ice sheets as they moved across the area and eventually melted, about 15 000 years ago. These deposits consist of boulders, stones, sand and clay. They blanket the landscape and may form mounds known as drumlins.

How the story starts

The landscape looks the way it does because of millions of years of Earth history, from the formation of the oldest rocks to the development of peat after the last ice age. The story in this part of Northumberland began about 500 million years ago.

The fold-out geological map

The distribution of the different rocks is shown on the fold-out map at the back of this book. Compare this with the satellite image of the area to see the obvious influence these rocks have had in shaping the modern landscape.

Beginnings

A 420 million year-old frontier

Deep in the Earth's crust beneath the Roman frontier of Hadrian's Wall lies a much more ancient boundary – a zone in the rocks that marks where two continents collided over four hundred million years ago. Scotland and England are on different portions of the Earth's crust which once lay thousands of miles apart on different continents, separated by a wide ocean. Over millions of years the two continents gradually moved towards each other, eventually colliding and destroying the ocean. In this collision, the southern continent was pushed beneath the northern one.

Plate tectonics

The outer layer of the Earth is a jigsaw of separate pieces, up to 100 km thick, known as plates. The rock below these plates is partially molten, and as it circulates it causes the plates above to move. These plates carry the continents and oceans, and are continually moving apart and colliding, in places at about the speed our fingernails grow! Where plates move apart, such as in the middle of the Atlantic today, molten rock rises and solidifies to create new ocean floor. Where plates collide, oceans are destroyed and mountain ranges are pushed up. The Himalaya are the result of India pushing up beneath Asia. Where plates grind past each other, the movement causes earthquakes along the boundary between the plates. All these processes are part of plate tectonics.

A - Scotland and the north of Ireland
B - England, Wales and south of Ireland

Iapetus – the great divide

500 million years ago land plants and animals had not yet evolved and the arrangement of continents and oceans was totally different from today. The pieces of Earth's crust that would eventually become Britain were separated by a wide ocean – known by geologists as the Iapetus Ocean – which was probably as wide as today's Atlantic. Scotland and the north of Ireland were part of a continent known as Laurentia, which also contained what is now North America and Greenland. To the south lay Avalonia, a small continent that contained England, Wales and the south of Ireland. Avalonia lay at the edge of a much larger continent, Gondwana, which included Africa, South America, India, Australia and Antarctica.

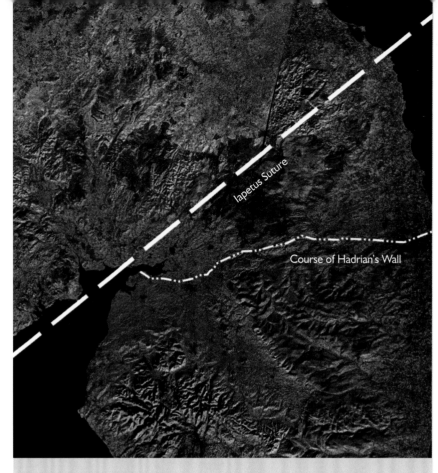

Iapetus Suture

Course of Hadrian's Wall

Vanishing ocean

About 470 million years ago the floor of the Iapetus Ocean started to descend into the depths of the Earth, in a process known as subduction. Volcanoes developed along the margins of the closing ocean, creating the volcanic rocks we see today in the Lake District, Wales and southern Scotland. As the ocean was consumed, the continents of Laurentia and Avalonia moved inexorably closer together.

Avalonia

Continental crunch

The continents of Laurentia and Avalonia eventually collided about 420 million years ago. The Iapetus Ocean disappeared and the mighty Caledonian Mountain range was forced up along the broad collision zone. These mountains were the Himalaya of their day but have now eroded away to their roots.

The Scottish Highlands are the best place to see the remnants of this ancient mountain chain. Britain was now joined along a great seam in the rocks. Known as the Iapetus Suture, this seam lies deeply buried beneath more recent rocks between Berwick-on-Tweed and the Solway Firth. The approximate position of this buried suture is shown on the satellite image above.

The scene is set...

After the collision, Britain became part of one great continent, sometimes called the Old Red Sandstone Continent. We lay just south of the Equator and the climate was hot and arid, similar to that of Arizona today. The Caledonian Mountains were being eroded away by flash floods, which deposited great thicknesses of red sands which hardened into the red sandstone we see today in the nearby Scottish Borders. The Old Red Sandstone Continent was then flooded by shallow seas and Britain was about to experience over 50 million years of tropical seas and rainforests.

Beginnings

Tropical seas and rainforests

Between 350 and 300 million years ago, the landmass that was to become Britain lay astride the Equator. Northern England was periodically covered in rainforests and tropical seas teeming with life. This was the Carboniferous Period of Earth history and nearly all the rocks we see in the Hadrian's Wall area were formed during this time.

Carboniferous world

This picture shows how geologists believe that the world would have looked about 350 million years ago. The pattern of land and sea was very different from today. Britain as we know it did not exist, but the piece of the Earth's crust that would eventually become Britain is shown astride the Equator.

Hot and wet

Imagine a hot and humid climate. Tropical seas full of bright corals, great river deltas draining out of mountains to the north, and dense rain forests alive with the sound of huge insects – this is Northumberland in the Carboniferous Period! But how do we know it was like this?

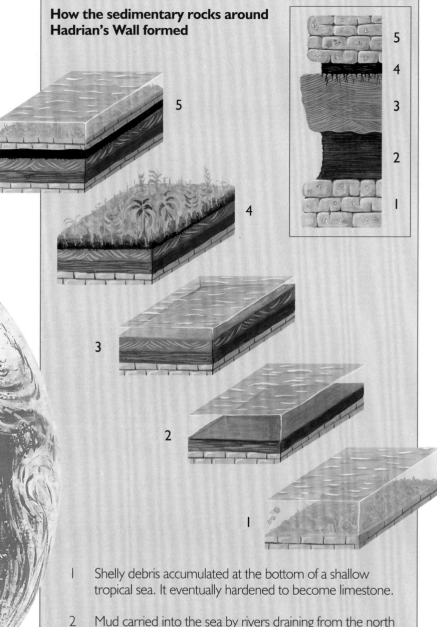

How the sedimentary rocks around Hadrian's Wall formed

5

4

3

2

1

1 Shelly debris accumulated at the bottom of a shallow tropical sea. It eventually hardened to become limestone.

2 Mud carried into the sea by rivers draining from the north settled on top of the limestone. This became mudstone.

3 River deltas advanced into the sea, depositing layers of sand. This hardened into sandstone.

4 Swamps and rainforests grew on the top of the river delta. Their remains became coal seams.

5 Sea levels rose, flooding the forests. Marine life returned and shelly debris covered the coal. And so the whole cycle started again...

Sea, delta, forest

We can reconstruct these ancient environments by looking at the rocks beneath our feet. In the Hadrian's Wall area these rocks are sedimentary rocks – limestone, mudstone, sandstone and coal. Limestone formed from the shelly remains of sea creatures. The mudstone and sandstone were once mud and sand, carried by large rivers into deltas. Coal seams are the remains of ancient buried forests. By looking at the way rocks are layered we can also work out the order in which things happened. Younger rocks lie above older rocks, so a limestone layer lying on top of a coal seam means that a sea overwhelmed and flooded a forest.

Rock cycles

Each repetition of limestone, mudstone, sandstone and coal is known by geologists as a 'cyclothem'. They are often called Yoredale cyclothems, after the old name for Wensleydale in North Yorkshire where they were first studied. These cyclothems have a profound influence on the landscape. Limestone and sandstone are hard rocks and resistant to weathering, whereas the softer mudstones tend to wear away more easily. This contrast in weathering produces the distinctive scarps and terraced hillsides of parts of the Pennines and Northumberland.

Where to go

Haltwhistle Burn
[NY713 659 to NY708 653]
The steep banks expose sections through parts of the 'cyclothems' described here, with especially good sections through the Great Limestone and its overlying mudstone and sandstone.

Limestone

Corals and crinoids

The shallow tropical sea that covered northern England about 350 million years ago, during the Carboniferous Period, would have been similar to the present-day Bahamas. Marine animals such as corals, sponges, crinoids, brachiopods and bivalves flourished in these warm, clear waters. We would recognise some of these animals today – but others are long extinct. Their remains – made of calcium carbonate like modern sea shells and corals – accumulated on the sea floor, eventually hardening into limestone. Evidence for the life in these long-vanished seas can be found in the form of fossils, the traces or bodies of ancient creatures preserved in rock.

▶ Reconstruction of a Carboniferous tropical sea

Crinoids – starfish on stalks

Swaying thickets of crinoids, also known as 'sea lilies', would have been a common sight in these tropical seas. Despite their name they were not plants – in fact they were related to starfish and sea urchins. Anchored to the sea bed, crinoids had long waving tentacles which captured small planktonic creatures drifting in the currents. Crinoids had skeletons made of many small disc-like plates of calcium carbonate. When they died and the soft tissue rotted, these plates fell apart. This photograph shows an unusually well preserved fossil of the crinoid *Woodocrinus* found near Matfen. Normally, all you can find are the separate plates, like scattered beads from a broken necklace.

Ooze turns to stone

When the Carboniferous sea creatures died their remains accumulated in layers on the seabed. These accumulations consisted of fragments of shells, corals, algae and crinoids and a limy ooze from microscopic animals. Some animals lived within this soft layer, burrowing in the sediment and mixing it up. The ooze compacted and hardened under the weight of layers above. Eventually, over millions of years, it became the solid limestone we see today. You may notice that the limestone around Hadrian's Wall is mid to dark grey, rather than the very pale grey limestones in the Yorkshire Dales. This is because the limestone in Northumberland is rather dirty – when it was forming it was mixed with mud and silt washing in from land nearby.

Molluscs

Molluscs include the great variety of bivalves, shellfish like modern cockles, mussels and scallops. They are filter feeders and would have lived on organic debris floating in the seawater or in the bottom sediment. Other molluscs that lived in Carboniferous seas included the coiled shelled goniatites and nautiloids which swam in the water. Goniatites were ancestors of the ammonites which became so important in later geological periods.

▲ Bivalve (above)
Goniatite (below)

Brachiopods

Like their modern relatives, the brachiopods in these ancient seas had thick shells and fed by filtering microscopic animals out of seawater. Brachiopods, such as the spirifer shown here, are some of the commonest fossils to be found in the Hadrian's Wall area.

Corals

Some corals were solitary, whereas others lived in reef-forming colonies. Like modern corals, they grew in many different shapes, from cups and horns to fans and platforms.

▼ Coral in limestone at Tipalt Burn

Where to go

Walltown Quarry [NY 669 660]
Good examples of the brachiopod spirifer can be seen near the start of the Hard Rock Trail.

North bank of the Tipalt Burn [NY679 679]
Beautifully preserved corals, brachiopods, crinoids and other fossils are exposed in an old limestone quarry 2.5 km east of Thirlwall Castle.

Milecastle Inn [NY717 661] and Crindledykes [NY781 670]
Good examples of natural limestone crags and disused quarries can be seen near the Milecastle Inn and around Crindledykes.

Limestone

Rocks for burning and building

Like many of the area's rocks, limestone is not just important as part of the natural landscape. As a valuable raw material, it has been quarried for centuries to produce lime, for improving grassland, and for making lime mortar. Lime burning dates from at least Roman times. Scattered around the countryside are many old limestone quarries, with adjoining limekilns. Today, lime is still used to improve acidic upland soils and the traditional use of lime mortar continues in the restoration of old buildings.

▲ The Four Fathom Limestone near Milecastle Inn

What's in a name?
Centuries ago miners and quarrymen recognised individual limestone beds and gave them names based on their appearance, thickness or location. For example, the Great Limestone is the thickest and most prominent limestone in the area, the Four Fathom Limestone is named for its thickness (miners and quarrymen often measured in fathoms – 1 fathom=6 feet [1.8 metres]), and the Cockleshell Limestone contains abundant fossil brachiopod shells. The names they gave the limestones were later adopted by geologists and are still used today.

Sweetening the soil
Limestone typically supports rich grassland. Early farmers recognised this and realised the value of lime as a soil improver. For centuries limestone was quarried to produce lime for 'sweetening' acidic soils. In upland country such as this, 'liming' was carried out nearly every year, creating a big demand for lime. Originally a cottage industry, lime burning grew into a major local industry in the 19th century.

◀ Cows and limekiln at Walltown

Lime for mortar

Lime was a vital ingredient in traditional mortar, and huge quantities would have been required for the area's castles, churches and farms. Two thousand years ago, enormous amounts would have been needed to build Hadrian's Wall, requiring a well-organised network of quarries and kilns. Roman tablets discovered at Vindolanda describe the burning of stone to make lime. Lime mortar is used today in the restoration and conservation of old buildings, such as Thirlwall Castle (pictured left).

▲ Detail of stonework inside Crindledykes limekiln

The limekiln

To produce lime, limestone has to be burnt at a high temperature. In this area, local coal and limestone were burnt together in kilns at temperatures of up to 1000°C. Carbon dioxide in the limestone was driven off, leaving calcium oxide, or quicklime. The quicklime was soaked or 'slaked' with water to produce slaked lime, or hydrated lime, which could then be spread on the land. You can see many good examples of limekilns in this area. They are usually built of sandstone blocks, and some include locally made firebricks.

▼ Crindledykes limekiln

Where to go

Crindledykes limekiln [NY781 670]
A fine group of limekilns, restored by Northumberland National Park Authority, stands by the roadside, adjoining the limestone quarries.

Ryal [NZ019 743]
Old limestone quarries and the remains of kilns can be seen east of the village.

Thirlwall Castle [NY659 662]
The walls show the recent use of traditional lime mortar in restoration work.

Limestone

Crags, pavements and sinkholes

Rainwater is slightly acidic because it dissolves carbon dioxide from the atmosphere forming a very weak solution of carbonic acid. Limestone is made of calcium carbonate ($CaCO_3$) and is soluble in acid. When rain falls on limestone it gradually dissolves it, forming such features as limestone pavement, sinkholes and caves. In areas of thick, pure limestone, such as the Yorkshire Dales, these features are spectacularly developed. Around Hadrian's Wall, where the limestones are thinner, these features are more subtle, although even here limestone has a profound and very distinctive effect on the shape of the land and on the plants that grow on it.

Limestone crags

Several separate layers of limestone – some up to 10 m thick – occur within the Hadrian's Wall area. Despite its soluble nature, limestone is actually quite a hard rock which resists erosion much better than mudstone and even some sandstones. As a result many of the limestone layers weather to form lines of low crags along the steep northern faces of escarpments. The low areas between the escarpments are underlain by soft, easily eroded mudstones.

 The fold-out geological map

Notice how the outcrops of limestone shown on the geological map coincide with the craggy ridges visible across the area.

▼ Natural outcrop of the Eelwell Limestone, modified by quarrying near Moss Kennels

Sinks and springs

As rainwater seeps through limestone it gradually dissolves the rock, widening joints and cracks. Eventually small underground caves may form. Collapse of the ground surface above these cavities produces distinctive hollows in the ground, known as sinkholes. If you are standing above limestone crags look out for small funnel-shaped or basin-like depressions in the nearby fields. Surface streams may 'sink' underground down these holes and flow underground through the limestone for hundreds of metres. In places where impervious rock, such as mudstone, lies beneath limestone, water flowing through the limestone is forced to break through to the surface, often forming a line of springs.

◀ Sinkhole north of Sewingshields

▲ Outcrop of well-jointed Lower Bath-House Wood Limestone in the River North Tyne, Barrasford

Limestone pavement

Where limestone outcrops have been stripped bare by ice sheets, the numerous vertical joints in the rock may be widened by solution in rain water, creating the distinctive habitat known as 'limestone pavement'. These joints are called 'grykes'; the upstanding masses between the joints are called 'clints'. Limestone pavement is very rare in Northumberland, but a small example can be seen near Broomlee Lough (above). The grykes provide a unique habitat for a variety of unusual plants.

Where to go

Broomlee Lough [NY788 700]
Limestone pavement occurs on the north side of the lough, near the boathouse.

Hallpeat Moss [NY727 656]
A large sinkhole into the Little Limestone can be seen from the footpath SW of Hallpeat Moss, east of the Milecastle Inn.

Military Road [NY807 695]
Limestone crags, often partly modified by small old quarries, are visible from the Military Road east of Housesteads.

Limestone

Living on limestone

Outcrops of limestone in the Hadrian's Wall area support more plant species than the more acidic grasslands and improved pasture found on other rocks.

Green and pleasant

Limestone grassland often looks like a splash of bright green in the landscape. We have already mentioned that farmers have long recognised that finer grasses grow on lime-rich soil than on acid soils. This led to the practice of 'sweetening' the soil by regular spreading of slaked lime, produced locally from countless small limekilns. To maintain the fertility of such 'improved' land, liming is still practised today, though powdered limestone rather than burnt lime is used.

▼ *Caloplaca saxicola*

Colourful variety

A variety of plant species grows in limestone areas including some that are rarely found elsewhere. Examples of plants found on limestone in the Hadrian's Wall area are salad burnet, fragrant orchid, fairy flax, thyme, eyebrights, autumn gentian, common rock rose, small scabious, hoary plantain and quaking grass. Grass of Parnassus and devil's bit scabious are often found in wet areas that have a limestone influence.

Some ferns such as maidenhair spleenwort are found growing on lime mortar and on limekilns, and some lichens, for example *Caloplaca saxicola,* are found exclusively on calcareous rocks.

1. Lichens *Xanthoria parietina*
   and *Diplica canescens*
2. Grass of Parnassus
3. Fragrant orchid
4. Eyebright
5. Thyme
6. Autumn gentian
7. Devil's bit scabious
8. Common rock rose
9. Maidenhair spleenwort

Animals in shells

Some animals are also typically associated with limestone. For example, the white-clawed crayfish (below), Britain's only native crayfish, will only live in lime-rich water. It occurs in some of the loughs that are fed by streams carrying lime in solution from nearby limestone outcrops, notably Broomlee Lough. This rare and protected species today depends upon the limestones formed 350 million years ago, from long-extinct sea creatures. Other invertebrates that need calcium for their shells, such as snails, are often found in greater numbers and varieties in limestone areas than elsewhere.

Where to go

Crindledykes East Quarry [NY784 673]
Limestone grassland and limestone flora occur in this old quarry. A Northumberland Wildlife Trust (NWT) Reserve.

Sewingshields [NY810 713]
Distinctly green limestone grassland can be seen from the footpath north of Sewingshields.

Broomlee Lough [NY788 700]
A small area of limestone pavement with distinctive plants is present on the north side of the lough, near the boathouse.

Gunnerton Nick [NY784 672]
Limestone and Whin Sill grassland can be seen in this Site of Special Scientific Interest.

Sand and Mud

Ancient mud, fossil soil, firebricks and iron ore

Mudstones, rocks which began life as ancient muds, form a large part of the 'layer-cake' of rocks in the Hadrian's Wall area. Despite being common, they are rarely seen at the surface. This is mainly because they are weak rocks which weather easily and do not form conspicuous exposures. Nonetheless, mudstones are extremely important in forming the landscape. Because they weather so readily, they commonly form belts of low ground between ridges of more resistant limestones or sandstones. As mudstones are impervious, outcrops are commonly marked by poorly drained or boggy ground.

Fossil soils

Some beds of mudstone and sandstone, which lie immediately beneath coal seams, contain an abundance of fossilised roots, giving clear evidence that they were the soils on which the coal-forming vegetation grew. These fossilised soils are known as 'seatearths'.

▼ *Stigmaria* root traces in a seatearth

▼ Layer of dark mudstone overlying limestone at Mootlaw Quarry

Firebricks and plant pots

Seatearths commonly have a chemical composition well-suited to the making of firebricks which will withstand very high temperatures. Known as 'fireclays' or locally 'seggar', these rocks can also be used for making a variety of other clay products. Fireclays were once worked at Haltwhistle and Bardon Mill, sometimes as a by-product of coal mining, for making firebricks, glazed drainpipes and sanitary wares. Bardon Mill Pottery (pictured right) today makes glazed pots using clay quarried as a by-product of opencast coal mining in east Northumberland.

Ancient muds

Mudstone is a rock composed of clay particles, deposited as mud in the sea or within a river delta. The term 'shale' is commonly applied when the rock splits easily into thin sheets or layers. Local miners sometimes referred to shales as 'plate'. Shales and mudstones may contain well-preserved fossils of shells or plants, indicating the environment in which they were deposited.

Iron ores

Some mudstones contain layers of nodules composed of the iron carbonate mineral siderite, known as 'clay-ironstone'. The examples pictured are from Brackies Burn. Similar ironstones that include appreciable quantities of coaly matter are known as 'blackband ironstones'. Both 'clay ironstones' and 'blackband ironstones' have been worked as iron ores in the Hadrian's Wall area. Old quarries may be seen on Cawfields Common and in the Honeycrook Burn, near Chesterwood. It is possible, though it cannot be proved, that the Romans worked these ores.

Where to go

Bardon Mill Pottery [NY779 646]
A working pottery making a variety of plant pots and containers.

Haltwhistle Fireclay Works [NY709 645]
Remains of the works adjoin the footpath at the foot of the Haltwhistle Burn.

Chesterwood [NY823 650]
Overgrown old quarries for 'blackband ironstone' adjoin the minor road at the crossing of the Honeycrook Burn, west of Chesterwood.

Lees Hall Quarry, Haltwhistle Burn [NY707 652]
A fine example of a 'seatearth', or fossil soil, beneath a thin coal seam, is exposed in the quarry face.

Sand and Mud

Rivers of sand

The tropical seas that once covered the Hadrian's Wall area were periodically choked by mud, silt and sand. These sediments were washed into the sea by large rivers draining off land that lay to the north. The rivers formed huge deltas that built out into the sea. The mud, silt and sand settled out, swamping the coral reefs and crinoid thickets. These layers of sediment eventually hardened into mudstone, siltstone and sandstone. The sand grains and structures contained within these rocks are fingerprints of the past, enabling us to piece together ancient environments and processes.

Deltas

The rivers that drained into the seas that once covered Northumberland formed large deltas, probably similar to the modern Mississippi Delta. A delta is a wide, flat, fan-shaped accumulation of sediment deposited where a river enters the sea. New land is created as the river dumps its load of sediment. Over time, the delta builds out into the sea depositing river sediments such as silt and sand on top of sea floor deposits such as limestone, as shown in this reconstruction. The Carboniferous deltas of northern England became colonised by lush swamps and rainforests, as we shall see later.

A world in a grain of sand

As the soft sands were buried by more sediments the sand grains were squashed together and eventually became cemented by minerals which infilled the spaces between the grains. The grains in a sandstone are more than just ancient sand. Each one is a relic of a long-vanished, eroded landscape and has its own story to tell. The sandstones of this area are usually composed almost entirely of grains of the mineral quartz. This picture, magnified 25 times, is of a very thin slice of sandstone, 0.03 mm thick, photographed under the microscope in polarised light. The quartz grains show as yellow, grey or white areas cemented together by much smaller amounts of other minerals including clays. These sand grains were once part of rocks which formed a landmass that lay to the north of what is now Northumberland, about 325 million years ago. Rivers brought the grains to the coast, where they were deposited in a delta.

Sandstone at Queen's Crag

From riverbed to rocky crag

Being a hard, resistant rock, sandstone tends to form upstanding ridges and crags. Strange though it may seem, the sandstone crags and hills of the area are the remains of river beds and channels that existed all those millions of years ago.

The fold-out geological map

The outcrops of the main sandstones are shown on the fold-out geological map

Ripple marks

Visit any sandy beach today when the tide has gone out and you will almost certainly see that the sand has a rippled surface. These ripples form in shallow water as currents gently agitate and move the sand. Similar processes were at work on the Carboniferous deltas of northern England. When such rippled sand surfaces are covered by sediment they may be preserved as the sand becomes compacted and hardened into sandstone. Fossilised ripple marks are surprisingly common in sandstones. Extremely fine examples may be seen in parts of the woodland which now occupies the long-abandoned workings of Black Pasture Quarry, near Chollerford (below). So good is the preservation here, that even casts of sand thrown up by burrowing worms 325 million years ago are faithfully preserved.

Where to go

Haltwhistle Burn [NY708 652]
Excellent sections through thick beds of sandstone are exposed in the burn.

Thorngrafton Common [NY787 666]
Thick sandstone beds form a series of impressive scarp features.

Black Pasture Quarry [NY930 698]
Excellent ripple-marked surfaces may be seen in the disused and overgrown parts of the quarry.

King's and Queen's Crags [NY795 706] [NY796 711]
These sandstone crags can be seen from the Pennine Way at Cragend and are on Open Access Land.

Sand and Mud

Heather, lichens and bats

Outcrops of sandstone are commonly marked by expanses of acidic or neutral grassland. Some of the soils may be rather waterlogged and support tussocky purple moor grass, mat grass and rushes, commonly accompanied by bilberry, tormentil and heath bedstraw. Heather (pictured right) grows on more free-draining ground, though its occurrence here is much less extensive than further north on the Fell Sandstone outcrops around Rothbury and in the Cheviots.

Lichens

Many lichens are very particular about the rock they will grow on. The species illustrated here are all found on sandstone crags and walls of buildings. When buildings or walls are restored it is important to replace stones the same way round as sunlight and humidity also have a role to play in where lichens grow.

 Cladonia macilenta

▶ *Hypogymnia physodes*

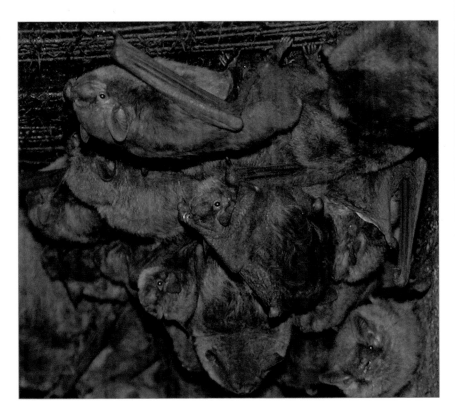

▲ Pipistrelle bats

▲ Peregrine falcon

▸ Raven

Birds and bats

Sandstone crags may provide nesting opportunities for many birds. Peregrine falcons and, in recent years, ravens have been spotted and it is hoped that they may become more common in the Hadrian's Wall area.

Birds such as house martins and swifts nest on farmhouses and barns and a variety of bats also use them as roosts. Although these species are not confined to sandstone buildings, many of the structures in the area are built from sandstone so the animals naturally use what is there.

Where to go

Thirlwall Castle [NY659 662]
A variety of lichens grow on the walls. Swifts nest here and bats may be seen leaving the building at dusk in the summer months.

Housesteads area [NY781 695]
Heather can be seen from the Pennine Way. The best time to look is when it is in flower, between August and September.

Examine walls to see lichens and, although it is hard to tell species apart, it is interesting to view the growth patterns and colours – look at the different types on different sides of walls and buildings.

Building with Stone

Barns and battlements

The area's natural landscape of distinctive hills, valleys, crags, mires and covering vegetation reflects the underlying rocks. Just as much a part of this landscape are the castles, churches, farms, cottages, barns, drystone walls and the wealth of Roman structures, including Hadrian's Wall itself. These too derive their individual style and character from these local rocks. For almost as long as humans have inhabited the area, local stone has been employed to give shelter to people and animals. With only a few exceptions, the preferred stone employed in building is sandstone.

The Roman design brief

Any major civil engineering project today requires careful planning based on an understanding of the site and of the properties of the materials available for its construction. Clear specifications of the materials to be used are needed to guide the designers, suppliers and builders. Like their modern counterparts, the Roman engineers would have faced these same design challenges.

The design of Hadrian's Wall called for a large supply of blocks of facing stone with a regular size and shape, with much larger quantities of rubble needed for the Wall's core. However, despite choosing to build long stretches of the Wall along the outcrop of the Whin Sill dolerite, the engineers realised that this rock could not be dressed easily into blocks of the required size and shape. Instead, they chose the abundant local sandstone as their building material.

For the rubble core of the Wall, where size and shape of the blocks was not important, fragments of sandstone and other easily available rocks, including dolerite, were used.

▼ Squared blocks of sandstone in Hadrian's Wall at Housesteads

Tablets on stone

Nisi rogas Voconti[...
Ut lepidem exp[...
Rogo ut rescri[bas
Quid veils me [...
Opto bene [valeas

Quem modum carrulorum
Missurus sis domine
Deliberare tecum debes
Ad lapidem portandum
Voconti enim centu[....
Carrulis uno die la..[...

Unless you ask
Vocontius to sort out
the stone, he will not
do it. I ask you to write
back what you want
me to do. I pray that
you are in good health.

.. you ought to decide, my lord, what
quantity of wagons you are going to
send to carry stone. For the century
of Vocontius…on one day with
wagons …..

We know a lot about Hadrian's Wall due to the
Vindolanda tablets – a series of letters written in Roman
times on wooden bases and wax tablets. Tablet 316,
illustrated here, is about the transport of stone.

Roman quarries

The enormous quantities of sandstone used in the
building of the Wall were, wherever possible, obtained
locally from a large number of quarries sited at intervals
along its course. In some cases it is possible to match the
stone used in the Wall with a particular sandstone bed,
or group of beds, though many of the local sandstones
are not sufficiently distinctive to enable their source to
be located precisely.

A few quarries can be reliably identified as being sites of
Roman working, mainly through authentic Roman
inscriptions carved on their faces, or from artefacts
recovered from them. However, it remains impossible
to identify the great majority of Roman quarry sites.

Particularly large blocks of stone for specific purposes,
such as those in the bridge which carried the Wall across
the River North Tyne at Chollerford, or for altars, were
supplied from a comparatively small number of quarries
capable of providing such large pieces. In these cases stone
may have been transported for considerable distances.

▼ Roman sandstone quarry on Thorngrafton Common

Where to go

Vindolanda [NY773 664]
Roman tablets discovered here can
be seen in the museum. Roman
quarries, including Roman graffiti,
can be seen high on the hilltop east
of Vindolanda.

Fallowfield Fell [NY937 687]
Roman carvings are to be seen on
sandstone outcrops at Written Crag.

Brocolitia [NY860 712]
Large stone altars can be seen in this
ancient temple.

Any part of Hadrian's Wall provides
ample evidence of the Roman style
of stone dressing and masonry.

Building with Stone

Stone through the centuries

As a World Heritage Site, Hadrian's Wall is today a treasured and protected structure, though it was not always so. Once abandoned, the Wall and its associated structures became an easy source of ready-shaped building blocks. Why go to the trouble and expense of quarrying and dressing new stone when ready-made blocks were there in abundance, merely for the taking?

Ready-made building blocks

A characteristic feature of much of the Wall is the distinctive shape and size of the sandstone blocks of which it is built. Typically square in outline, these blocks are easily recognised where they have been incorporated into later buildings.

In places, larger blocks of obvious Roman origin, including stone altars, have been incorporated into later buildings. Part of an altar, together with other carved and worked stones, forms part of the fabric of the crypt at Hexham Abbey.

▼ Extensive re-use of Roman stones can be seen at Thirlwall Castle

Drystone walls

Like much of upland northern England, this area has many miles of drystone wall. These were typically built of the nearest available stone, either clearance stones off adjoining fields, or rock from small pits opened in sandstone outcrops along the courses of the walls. In many places blocks from the Wall itself were used, as seen at Sewingshields farm (above).

Quality stone

Whereas almost any reasonably durable sandstone will suffice for rough walling, some of the area's sandstones occur in thick beds which exhibit grain size, colour and other properties which make them attractive for use as dressed stone for high quality building work. Large quarries at Fourstones and Chollerford provided stone for use across northern England and beyond, particularly during the 19th century. Stone is still worked from Black Pasture Quarry at Chollerford.

▼ Men standing beside Hunter's Patent Stone Dressing Machine at Fourstones

▲ Quarrymen beside a vertical boiler on tracks at Prudham Quarry near Fourstones, probably providing steam for cutting equipment

Raising the roof

Some sandstones split readily into very thin slabs only a centimetre or two thick, making them suitable for use as roofing slabs as shown here near Chesterwoods.

Excavation of debris at many Roman sites suggests that clay tiles were a common roofing material. From the fragments recovered it seems that glacial clay and perhaps some mudstones and shales were the raw materials for tile making. The sites of the clay pits and firing kilns are not known.

Keeping warm

At Chesters Fort bath house, shaped blocks of tufa were used in the vaulting of the hot room. This porous, light-weight rock occurs as deposits around lime-rich springs. Although known to occur in parts of Northumberland, no nearby deposit could have provided the amount needed at Chesters. The stone seems likely to have been imported, perhaps from Europe. What, then, was the source of this stone, and why was it so special? Perhaps its lightness and thermal insulating properties appealed to the Roman builders. An early ancestor of the modern breeze block, perhaps?

Where to go

Haltwhistle [NY70 64]
Many houses are built of sandstone and locally made bricks.

Hexham Abbey [NY935 641]
The crypt includes re-used Roman stones, including part of a sandstone altar.

Black Pasture Quarry, Chollerford [NY930 698]
The faces that were worked for sandstone can be seen in the abandoned parts of the quarry, which can be visited.

Roman stones may be seen throughout the area in buildings such as Thirlwall Castle, in several churches (Corbridge Church uses much Roman stone), in farm houses and even in drystone walls around fields.

Coal

Black forest

Tropical rainforests and swamps flourished on the fertile mud, silt and sand of the deltas that once covered northern England. These vast forests stretched from Europe to North America and would have been as dense and luxuriant as the Amazon rainforest today. The forests were periodically drowned when the sea level rose, but as the deltas were rebuilt the forests grew again. Each time a forest was submerged and buried under marine deposits, it became compressed and hardened into a coal seam. Fossil plants preserved in coal and the surrounding rocks give us a glimpse of the variety of plant life in these ancient forests.

Scorpions and dragonflies

Imagine standing in a Carboniferous rainforest. Birds and mammals have yet to evolve, and even dinosaurs will not appear for another 100 million years. But this forest would not have been silent. It would have been alive with the whirr of insect wings and the scuttling of scorpions, spiders and giant cockroaches on the forest floor. Amphibians the size of alligators lived by pools and riverbanks, and dragonflies the size of hawks flitted through the branches.

Giant mosses and horsetails

Many of the trees of the Carboniferous forests were the ancestors of today's club mosses, ferns and horsetails. Unlike their modern relatives some of these plants towered above the forest floor. The club mosses were up to 30 m high, the height of a large oak tree today. The forests would have been hot and humid places, dense with undergrowth and creepers, and pervaded by the smell of rotting vegetation.

▼ Close up of modern horsetail

Fossil forest

We can still get glimpses of those ancient forests, now preserved as seams of black coal. Perfect impressions of leaves, cones, bark and roots tell us what sort of plants grew. One of the more common types of plant was a giant club moss, known as *Lepidodendron*. Fossilised tree stumps are occasionally found, such as that shown here from a colliery near Wallshield, and preserved today at the Once Brewed Visitor Centre.

Black forest

The coal forests grew in soils that are often preserved as layers of the rock known to the miners as 'seatearth'. We have already seen the use of these rocks in making pots and bricks.

When trees died they fell to the forest floor, eventually building up a thick layer of rotting vegetation. It takes about 10 m of dead plants to make a 1 m thick coal seam. Scientists have estimated that this amount of plant material requires about 7000 years of forest growth.

▷ Coal seam resting on seatearth at Lees Hall Quarry

Where to go

Lees Hall Quarry, Haltwhistle Burn [NY707 652]
A thin coal seam, together with its sandy seatearth, is clearly exposed in the face of the quarry.

Once Brewed Visitor Centre [NY752 669]
The fossilised trunks of several Carboniferous trees, recovered from a nearby colliery, stand in the car park.

Coal

Coal mining

The peaceful country of the Hadrian's Wall area seems far removed from the industrial landscape of the coalfield areas of Tyneside and south Northumberland. However, this apparently unspoilt tranquillity belies the fact that the coal seams within its rocks were being mined until very recently.

Although most of the area's coal seams are rather older and thinner than those of the main coalfield, a few seams have been thick enough, and of sufficiently good quality, to mine.

Early working

It is not known when coal was first worked in the area. However, as coal fragments have been discovered in excavations at several Roman sites, it seems that the Romans must have discovered seam outcrops in the neighbourhood and worked them for fuel.

▼ A set of full tubs coming out of Fourstones mine. The older man walking at front of the set is carrying a dreg, a wood or iron stave, to put between the spokes of a tub wheel to prevent it from turning and act as a brake. He is safe if the hauling rope breaks. The younger man, riding on the set, is in a more dangerous position

A putter pushes (or 'puts') a tub of coal away from the working face. He is being watched by a Deputy, who among other duties was employed in setting timber for the safety of the workmen

A hewer, the actual coal digger, working coal with a pick

Recent working

Little is known of coal working until the 19th century. By then coal was being mined at several places in the area. The main seam worked lay a few metres beneath the Little Limestone, known locally as the Little Limestone Coal. The arduous and dangerous manual labour involved is illustrated in the black and white photographs here from Fourstones Colliery, which operated from the early nineteenth century until 1927. There is little to be seen of this colliery today. More conspicuous are the remains, including the distinctive chimney, of the colliery near the head of the Haltwhistle Burn.

▲ Thirlwall Colliery drops which enabled coal to be tipped from narrow gauge colliery wagons into main line railway trucks

The aftermath of coal mining

Unlike the main coalfield of north-east England, where extensive surface subsidence is common over old underground workings, the underground workings in the Hadrian's Wall area show little obvious evidence of surface collapse. Another feature of former coal mining areas is, however, locally apparent. Water draining from old coal workings may bring dissolved minerals, most commonly iron, to the surface where they may be precipitated as bright orange-brown ochreous deposits. Lagoons to treat water discharging from the most recent workings in the area, at Blenkinsopp Colliery, have been built on the north side of the A69 near Blenkinsopp Castle.

Where to go

Haltwhistle Burn [NY710 656]
The remains of a small colliery, with its fine stone chimney, are visible near the head of the burn.

Milecastle Inn [NY715 657 to NY718 658]
A conspicuous line of old shafts marks the outcrop of the Little Limestone Coal alongside the footpath south and east of the Inn.

Crindledykes limekilns [NY781670]
'Rusty' water draining from colliery spoil often trickles onto the road.

Grindon Lough [NY806 676] and Chainley Burn [NY772 658]
Small spoil heaps mark the position of long-abandoned underground coal mines.

Thirlwall Colliery Coal Drops [NY647 667]
This large structure can be seen north-west of Greenhead.

Whinstone

Hot rock, crystals and columns

The Whin Sill is one of northern England's most famous and impressive natural features. Rising from the surrounding landscape, its outcrop is marked by long ridges and formidable, north-facing crags which formed an ideal rampart for Hadrian's Wall. The story of the Whin Sill's formation is as spectacular as its appearance in today's landscape. Tell-tale signs of the Whin Sill's fiery birth can still be seen within its cliffs and crags.

Molten rock

Stretching and splitting of the Earth's crust about 295 million years ago caused huge amounts of molten rock, or magma, to well up from deep within the Earth at temperatures of over 1000°C. This magma did not reach the surface, but was forced between the layers of limestone, sandstone and mudstone. As it cooled and solidified it formed sheets, up to 30 metres thick, of a hard black rock known as dolerite. Dolerite is an example of an intrusive igneous rock – a rock formed by the cooling of magma beneath the Earth's surface. Known to generations of quarrymen, and later to geologists, as the Whin Sill, it is now exposed at the Earth's surface after millions of years of erosion.

Sandstone

Whin Sill dolerite

Mudstone

Limestone

Original sill

The term 'sill' is used by geologists throughout the world to describe a sheet of igneous rock which is roughly parallel to the layers of rocks into which it has been intruded. However, to a 19th century northern quarryman the word meant any more or less flat-lying layer of rock. 'Whin' was also a quarryman's term for a hard black rock. Thus 'Whin Sill' was a descriptive name meaning a layer of hard black rock. Geologists who studied the Whin Sill in the 19th century recognised its intrusive igneous nature, and the word 'sill' was adopted for all similar bodies of igneous rock worldwide. The Whin Sill thus has the distinction of being the original sill of geological science.

The fold-out geological map

On the geological map you will see the Whin Sill outcrop as a layer running more or less parallel with the outcrops of limestones and sandstones. If followed very carefully across the map, its change of level through different beds within the Carboniferous rocks can be detected. The narrow Haydon Bridge Dyke, and other small dykes, also related to the Whin Sill, can also be traced.

▼ The Whin Sill at Peel Crags

▲ A survey geologist examining the Haydon Bridge Dyke at Wydon Nabb near Haltwhistle in 1927

As well as forming huge, nearly horizontal, sheets of dolerite, in places the Whin Sill magma rose up along narrow vertical fractures, cooling to form narrow vertical wall-like bodies, known as dykes. One such dyke, known as the Haydon Bridge Dyke, runs along the Tyne valley from south of Haltwhistle to Haydon Bridge, where it was once quarried for roadstone.

Whinstone

Mineral kaleidoscope

Mineral mosaic

Although at first sight it appears to be just a dull black rock, if you look closely at a piece of fresh dolerite you can see that it is made up of many small crystals. The dark crystals are the mineral pyroxene and the pale crystals are feldspar. These crystals formed when the molten rock cooled. The minerals crystallized out of the magma, forming the solid interlocking mass of crystals we see today. When seen under the microscope in polarised light the Whin Sill is strikingly beautiful; slices of rock, so thin (0.03 mm thick) that they are transparent, look like miniature stained glass windows. The pieces of Whin Sill dolerite in these images are each about 2 mm across.

▼ Whin Sill showing columns, Sewingshields Crags

▲ Vesicles formed near the top of the Whin Sill at Walltown

Bubbles, cracks and columns

As the molten rock cooled and solidified, bubbles of gas trapped in the magma formed small cavities, or vesicles, in the rock. Some of these later became filled with minerals such as quartz and calcite. Vesicles in the Haydon Bridge Dyke were notable for beautiful crystals of purple quartz (amethyst) found in them.

In the final stages of cooling the hot dolerite contracted, producing vertical cracks, or joints, along which the rock breaks easily into columns. This is known as 'columnar jointing'. These columns are a prominent feature of the Whin Sill cliffs and quarry faces. Some columns are roughly hexagonal in cross-section and are similar to the spectacular examples at the Giant's Causeway in Northern Ireland.

Baked rocks

Molten rock at 1000°C has a huge effect on the rocks with which it comes into contact . When the Whin Sill was intruded into limestone, sandstone and mudstone, the intense heat baked and altered them. Sandstone and mudstone were hardened and recrystallized, and limestone turned into marble. It is thought that the Whin Sill took about 50 years to cool, so it had a long time to bake the surrounding rocks.

Where to go

Walltown Quarry [NY669 660]
Follow the Hard Rock Trail to discover columnar jointing, vesicles, and other features associated with the Whin Sill.

Cawfields Quarry [NY713 666]
A popular picnic site which shows many features typical of the Whin Sill, including columnar joints and vesicles.

Whinstone

A natural rampart

The escarpment formed by the outcrop of the Whin Sill dolerite provided the Roman engineers with an obvious natural defensive site for many kilometres along the central section of Hadrian's Wall.

The sombre north-facing crags expose spectacular examples of columnar-jointed dolerite and provide a number of important wildlife habitats. The near-vertical cliffs at Peel Crags, Walltown Crag and Steel Rigg are today popular with rock climbers.

▼ Hadrian's Wall above the Whin Sill cliff, with Crag Lough behind

A solid foundation

Although the Roman construction teams must have excavated huge amounts of loose dolerite blocks to establish their foundations, they were reluctant to use this abundant source of stone for building the Wall itself. As we have already seen, they selected the more easily worked local sandstones as the main construction material for the Wall and its associated buildings.

▶ The Wall at Peel Crags

Defeated by dolerite

Skilled though the Roman engineers were at breaking and moving hard rock, the dolerite of the Whin Sill proved too much for them at one point. Near Milecastle 30, at the place known as Limestone Corner (below), the vallum and its ditch were designed to cross the bare outcrop of the Whin Sill. Many large blocks of dolerite were excavated, no doubt with some difficulty. However, in places where it was necessary to break very large solid masses of this rock, even Roman determination and ingenuity were defeated. Several wedge holes testify to abortive attempts to break the rock (right). The ditch was left incomplete.

Where to go

Steel Rigg [NY757 676], Hotbank Crags [NY777 685] and Housesteads [NY787 688]
Just a few of the many places at which to see the spectacular crags of the Whin Sill.

Limestone Corner [NY825 706]
Evidence of the Romans' failure to excavate the Whin Sill dolerite.

Whinstone

Paving the way

Some of the characteristics that make the Whin Sill such an impressive part of the landscape also make it useful and commercially valuable. Its hardness and, more importantly, its resistance to becoming smoothed or polished by wear, are just the properties needed for surfacing modern roads.

For many years the dolerite of the Whin Sill, known to generations of Northumberland quarrymen simply as 'whinstone', has been worked at numerous places along its outcrop, and used to surface roads throughout northern England and beyond.

Setts and chippings

Today, as in the past, most of the Whin Sill quarried is crushed to make 'whinstone chippings'. These are used, either alone or coated in tar, for road surfacing. In addition, until at least the 1950s, several quarries made whinstone 'setts' – roughly squared blocks used for paving – sometimes, incorrectly, called 'cobbles'. Larger blocks were dressed to make kerbstones. As sett and kerbstone making was done by hand by highly skilled quarrymen, it eventually became uneconomic. Opened in 1876, Walltown Quarry was the largest 'whinstone' quarry on Hadrian's Wall and produced huge quantities of road chippings and setts for many years. As workable reserves of stone were exhausted the quarry was closed in 1976.

▼ Late 19th or early 20th century quarrymen at Walltown with tub, setts, kerbstones and whin chips

▲ Cawfields, still operating in 1950

▲ Cawfields today

East from Walltown, the rather smaller Cawfields Quarry closed in 1952. After its closure this much deeper quarry became flooded. Both quarries have been restored and landscaped as picnic areas and wildlife havens. The dark, deep waters of Cawfields are used as a training site by divers.

In the pictures of these quarries, taken when they were working, see how the working methods differ from the modern quarries. In particular, notice the tramways used to carry broken rock from the face to the crushing plant.

▲ Quarry plant of 'Spring field' Haydon Bridge

A forgotten industry

The vertical, wall-like body of Whin Sill dolerite, known as the Haydon Bridge Dyke, is concealed beneath glacial and river deposits along most of its course. However, it cropped out at the surface east of Haydon Bridge where it was quarried for roadstone for many years. The quarry had one of the earliest coating plants for 'Tarmac'. No sign of the workings can be seen today.

Where to go

Walltown [NY669 660] and Cawfields [NY713 666] quarries Both are examples of large abandoned quarries worked for roadstone and sett making. The 'Hard Rock Trail', has been laid out to introduce visitors to the local geology at Walltown.

Whinstone

Whinstone today

Quarrying for roadstone is an extremely important part of the area's economy, with four large working quarries at Keepershield, Barrasford, Swinburn and Divethill. With its sophisticated methods of blasting, crushing and quality control and its distribution network, today's quarrying industry is a far cry from the past. Modern techniques of dust suppression, noise control, careful planning of workings and restoration of worked-out areas, allow the industry to operate in harmony with local communities, wildlife and with minimum impact on the landscape. Indeed, most visitors to the area are unaware of the scale of this vital extractive industry in the heart of the Northumberland countryside.

▼ Rock is crushed to make aggregate at Barrasford Quarry

Not so smooth

With constant use, a road surface wears and becomes smooth. For safety it is obviously important that the surface does not become so smooth that skidding is a risk. One of the many properties required of a roadstone is the ability of the stone to maintain a suitably rough, or skid-free, surface as it wears. Technically this is known as a rock's Polished Stone Value (PSV), which can be measured and expressed numerically.

The dolerite of the Whin Sill typically has a high PSV, making it well-suited to surfacing roads. The high PSV results from the mineralogical composition of the rock. As we have seen, dolerite is composed of an intergrowth of different minerals. Whereas all are comparatively hard and resistant, each mineral differs from its neighbour in hardness, and wears at a different rate. As a result, the worn surface tends to remain rather rough – just what is needed on a road surface.

▲ Laying a modern blacktop road surface

Barrasford cottages

As we have seen, the Romans generally avoided the use of hard Whin Sill dolerite in their buildings. Successive generations of builders have also avoided its use, for the same reasons. However, near the former entrance of Barrasford Quarry, a small group of quarrymen's cottages, and the former quarry office, today stand as empty, but interesting, monuments to the rare local use of Whin Sill dolerite as a building stone (below).

Where to go

Barrasford Quarry cottages [NY909 740]
Rare examples of use of local dolerite in building.

To see the use of whinstone, look at any road in the area: it will almost certainly be surfaced with it.

The working whinstone quarries are well-screened and generally inconspicuous from most roads and many footpaths. However, when meeting lorries carrying roadstone, reflect on how important this rock is in making your road journey possible.

Local quarries occasionally have open days to explain working methods.

Whinstone

Sill life

The extremely hard dolerite of the Whin Sill does not weather easily, but usually gives rise to thin alkaline soils. Because these soils sometimes may resemble those of nearby, or adjacent, limestone outcrops, it can be difficult to tell if a plant is growing on the Whin Sill or adjacent limestone. Many of the same species grow in both soils but it is often those that are most drought resistant that thrive on the Whin Sill.

▶ Rue-leaved saxifrage
▶ Maiden pink

▼ Wild chives

A tasty rarity
In Northumberland wild chives is only found on the thin Whin Sill soils where it seems to out-compete grasses. It can be seen growing in cracks in the dolerite (below). Because this tasty herb is grazed by stock, the Northumberland National Park Authority has installed cages over some patches of the plant in an attempt to encourage the plants to flower and set seed.

▲ Biting stonecrop

Other sill plants

Other plants found on whinstone include rue leaved saxifrage, rock rose, thyme, mountain pansy, small flowered and long stalked cranesbill, maiden pink, biting stonecrop and wild onion. Many of these species, including chives, are classed as British Nationally Scarce Species.

▸ Mountain pansy

Birds

Like the sandstone crags, birds use the ledges for nesting sites. Kestrels (pictured right), jackdaws, peregrine falcons and ravens are all found in the area. United Kingdom legislation provides general protection for all nesting birds. Certain species, like the peregrine, are afforded special protection. Climbers help wildlife by avoiding the nesting season when crag nesting birds can be disturbed.

People

There is also human life on the sill. Many people walk along the Hadrian's Wall Trail which follows the Whin Sill ridge for much of its course. The jointed, vertical faces of the Whin Sill provide good climbing, such as the route shown here on Peel Crags.

Where to go

Gunnerton Nick [NY914 751]
Whin Sill and limestone grassland may be seen here.

Walltown Farm [NY680 665 and NY682 665]
Wild chives can be seen next to the road.

Peel Crags [NY757 676] and Highshield Crags [NY764 678]
These are well-known locations for climbing.

Minerals

Heavy metal

Ruined buildings, overgrown spoil heaps and an isolated row of miners' cottages are all that remain of a once thriving mining industry. Hidden in the rocks beneath the landscape are veins containing metal ores and other valuable minerals. For hundreds of years people mined lead in this area – even the Romans may have used local lead.

A wealth of lead

Originally it was the lead ore, galena, that attracted interest, but we don't know when it was first mined here. Although the Romans certainly used huge quantities of lead in their plumbing systems (our word 'plumbing' comes from the Latin word for lead – 'plumbum'), there is no proof that they ever worked these deposits but, as they were skilled metal workers, it seems inconceivable that they were unaware of the local ore. It may be no coincidence that Hadrian's Wall marks the northern limit of economic lead deposits in England.

Large scale lead mining here dates mainly from the 19th century, with large mines at Langley Barony, Settlingstones, Stonecroft and Fallowfield. A collapse in world lead prices towards the end of the 19th century forced the closure of most British lead mines, including those of this area.

Although the area's galena contains a little silver – usually around 30 to 60 parts per million – it is not known how much, if any, was recovered during smelting in the Hadrian's Wall area.

Galvanized into action

Associated with the galena at Langley Barony and Stonecroft was an abundance of the zinc ore, sphalerite. This was worthless in the 19th century and was dumped on the spoil heaps, but during the 1950s thousands of tons of sphalerite were extracted by reprocessing these heaps, leaving large accumulations of fine-grained spoil, or 'tailings'. One of the many uses of zinc is in coating steel – galvanizing.

What are veins?

Veins are sheet-like bodies of mineral that occupy more or less vertical cracks or fissures in the surrounding rocks. Most of these fissures are 'faults', cracks along which the rocks on either side have been displaced as a result of earth movements millions of years ago. Veins can vary from a few millimetres to over 10 metres in width, though most are only a few metres wide. In our area they are composed mainly of the barium minerals barytes ($BaSO_4$) and witherite ($BaCO_3$), with much smaller amounts of the ore minerals galena (PbS) and sphalerite or zinc blende ((Zn,Fe)S).

▼ Alf Angus (left) and Joe Hodgson drilling in the vein, Settlingstones Witherite Mine

How did veins form?

Deep in the Earth, rocks are saturated with water resembling concentrated sea water. This is a powerful solvent, capable of dissolving traces of a variety of chemical elements, including lead and zinc, which occur dispersed through the rocks. In this area heat from the granite that lies buried deep beneath the nearby North Pennines may have acted as a 'heat engine', warming these fluids and causing them to circulate through faults and fractures in a way similar to the water in a domestic central heating system flows through the pipes. As the fluids cooled, the dissolved minerals crystallised on the walls of the fissures, gradually building up the mineral veins. The area's veins are believed to have formed shortly after the injection of the Whin Sill, about 295 million years ago.

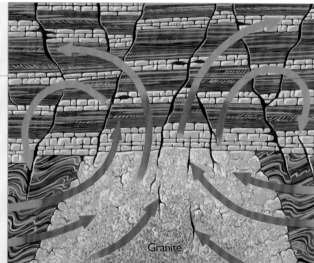

Granite

Special plants

Soils near old lead mines may contain high levels of lead and zinc, toxic to all but a few plants known as 'metallophytes' (literally 'metal loving'), which can tolerate these metals. Plants such as spring sandwort (sometimes called leadwort), alpine pennycress, thrift and much more rarely, Young's helleborine can be found near some old mine sites and on river shingles rich in lead and zinc minerals.

▲ Thrift (above)
▲ Alpine pennycress (above right)

▼ Spring sandwort

Where to go

Stonecroft Mine [NY854 689]
The brick-built Cornish engine house is a conspicuous landscape feature when seen from the Stanegate west of Newbrough.

Beltingham shingles [NY780 643]
A wide area of shingle on the south bank of the River South Tyne is a colourful site with a rich display of metallophyte plants in spring.

Stonecroft Mine and Beltingham River Shingles are SSSIs.

Spectacular examples of the area's minerals may be seen in museums such as Killhope, The North of England Lead Mining Museum, Weardale, and the Natural History Museum, London.

Minerals

Rare crystals and rat poison

As well as the ores of lead and zinc, the mineral veins contain much greater quantities of other minerals, known as gangue minerals, or as 'spar' by the miners. Although many of these are of no commercial value, in the late 19th century an unusual and valuable 'spar' mineral, witherite, was discovered in abundance in the mines at Settlingstones and Fallowfield, and a new and unique mining industry was born almost overnight.

Witherite

Although common in our area, especially at Settlingstones and Fallowfield, elsewhere in the world this is an extremely scarce mineral. Witherite, or natural barium carbonate ($BaCO_3$), is a white or cream-coloured mineral which is very heavy and looks slightly greasy. Its crystals are usually hexagonal prisms and pyramids. Beautiful specimens from Settlingstones and Fallowfield mines are found in many of the world's major mineral museums. Witherite was a valuable raw material used to make barium chemicals for the glass, paint and cement industries. It was also used in brick making, water softening, sugar processing and steel hardening.

▼ Witherite crystals from Fallowfield Mine

▲ Alstonite from Fallowfield Mine

Alstonite

Associated with the witherite at Fallowfield, another barium carbonate mineral was discovered in the 1830s. Research on specimens from both here and from a mine near Alston in the North Pennines, showed this to be a new mineral that eventually became known as alstonite. Chemically, this is a barium and calcium carbonate ($BaCa(CO_3)_2$). Like witherite it is very rare elsewhere in the world, but is found at several places in northern England, particularly at Fallowfield Mine, from which have come some of the finest examples known. Fallowfield Mine is today a Site of Special Scientific Interest because of this unusual mineral.

Witherite mining

Settlingstones Mine was originally a lead mine, producing the lead ore mineral galena. Then, in 1873, miners discovered a section of mineral vein consisting almost entirely of witherite, up to nine metres wide. After this discovery, Settlingstones Mine changed rapidly from lead ore to witherite production. It became the world's most important, and for long periods sole, commercial source of this unusual mineral. At its closure in 1968 the mine had produced 630 000 tons of witherite – almost half the total world output. Witherite was also mined from Fallowfield Mine until its closure in 1912.

Poisonous crystals

Witherite is toxic to most animals. Livestock, especially poultry, have been poisoned by eating grains of the mineral in soil. It was once ground up and used as a rat poison.

▼ Stock piles of witherite at Settlingstones mine in 1967

▲ The winding wheel from the Ellen shaft today at Fourstones

▲ Headgear at the Ellen Shaft, Settlingstones Mine. In its later years this was an alternative exit and ventilation shaft

Where to go

Settlingstones Cottages [NY846 686]
The miners' cottages can still be seen.

Settlingstones Mine [NY843 683]
A small pipe rising from the field, immediately south of the Stanegate, marks the site of Frederick Shaft, the main working shaft .

Fourstones [NY889 679]
The winding wheel from the Ellen Shaft has been preserved near the garage.

Fallowfield Dene [NY939 678]
The remains of the Fallowfield lead and witherite mine may be seen here.

Hidden History

The missing years

As we have seen, we can decipher parts of the long history of the Hadrian's Wall country by reading the evidence contained in its rocks. We have only a rather sketchy picture of our geological history before the Carboniferous period which began about 350 million years ago when the area which was to become Hadrian's Wall country lay somewhere close to the Equator. Since then we have continued our journey northwards to our present position. After the formation of the Whin Sill, about 295 million years ago, the evidence presented by rocks falls largely silent until the area was overridden by vast ice sheets as recently as around one million years ago.

This geological timeline highlights some of the events that were taking place both here in northern England, and elsewhere in the British Isles, throughout geological time.

Grey boxes indicate the periods represented by rocks and deposits in the Hadrian's Wall area.

Million years ago	Geological Period
0	**QUATERNARY AND HOLOCENE** Following the final melting of the ice, rivers and streams were re-established, woodland developed and humans came to inhabit the area.
0.01	**PLEISTOCENE** Global cooling resulted in ice age conditions which alternated with warmer periods known as 'interglacials'. Ice sheets advanced and retreated across the British Isles several times.
1.8	**NEOGENE** This was a period of uplift and erosion which shaped many features of the present landscape.
24	**PALAEOGENE** The opening of the north Atlantic was accompanied by volcanic activity in Ireland and western Scotland.
65	**CRETACEOUS** Much of what is now the British Isles, including the Hadrian's Wall area, lay beneath a warm shallow sea in which huge thicknesses of chalk were deposited. Later uplift and erosion have removed these from our area.

142	**JURASSIC** Dinosaurs lived along the coasts of shallow seas which covered much of what is now the British Isles. Sediments deposited at this time were later eroded from this part of northern England.
206	**TRIASSIC AND PERMIAN** Desert conditions and hot shallow seas covered what is now northern England. Rocks formed during these periods have long been eroded from this part of northern England.
290	**CARBONIFEROUS** The area that is now the British Isles straddled the Equator and was covered by tropical seas, wide coastal swamps and rainforests. Most of the rocks in the Hadrian's Wall area were formed at this time. Late in Carboniferous times as the Earth's crust was stretched, deep beneath the surface, the huge volumes of molten rock which became the Whin Sill were intruded. Shortly after the Whin Sill's intrusion, the area's mineral veins were formed.
354	**DEVONIAN** The Caledonian Mountains were eroded in a hot, arid climate. Volcanoes erupted in what is now the Cheviot Hills. Rocks formed during this period may lie buried deep beneath the area.
417	**SILURIAN** The continents of Laurentia and Avalonia finally collided, forming the Caledonian Mountains. Rocks formed during this period may lie buried deep beneath the area.
443	**ORDOVICIAN** Thick layers of mud and sand were deposited within the Iapetus Ocean. Huge volcanoes erupted in what is now the Lake District and North Pennines. Rocks formed during this period may lie buried deep beneath the area.
495	**CAMBRIAN** The Iapetus Ocean was created. In this were deposited thick layers of mud and sand. Rocks formed during this period may lie buried deep beneath the area.
545	**PRECAMBRIAN** The oldest rocks known on Earth are about 4000 million years old. The oldest rocks in the British Isles are the Lewisian gneisses of northern Scotland which are up to 3000 million years old. Primitive life first emerged on Earth about 3500 million years ago.
4600	**FORMATION OF THE EARTH**

Where to go

Chesters Walled Garden
[NY908 702]
Obviously we cannot see what has not been preserved in the geological record. However, one of the oldest and most unusual trees on the planet, the gingko (above), can be seen growing in the south of the Chesters Walled Garden. Although we do not know whether it grew in our area in ancient times, the ginkgo has survived on Earth little changed for over 200 million years. The earliest Gingkoales fossils have been dated back to the end of the Permian Period.

Ice

Ice sheets

Two million years ago, the world climate cooled rapidly, heralding the start of a series of ice ages. These cold, glacial periods alternated with warmer periods known as interglacials. We are currently in an interglacial that began about 11 000 years ago. As Britain succumbed to the cold, great ice sheets advanced from west to east across the Hadrian's Wall area. For thousands of years the British Isles were an uninhabitable expanse of ice, much like the interior of Greenland today. Beneath this icy blanket the land was being moulded – scraped by rocks frozen within the ice and by torrents of meltwater.

The ice arrives
In the last major ice age, which was at its peak about 20 000 years ago, glaciers and ice sheets advanced from the north to cover much of the British Isles. Ice reached as far south as the Bristol Channel. The ice was up to 2 km thick in Scotland and would have been nearly 1 km thick in the Lake District and across parts of Hadrian's Wall country. No land, except some of the highest peaks in Scotland and the Lake District, would have poked through.

Erratic movements
Boulders carried by glaciers and deposited away from their bedrock source are known as 'erratics'. By identifying the source of these boulders we can tell the directions of ice movement. A speckled pink and grey granite boulder (right) found near Thirlwall Castle came from the Criffel area in south-west Scotland. It was carried nearly 100 km from there by an ice sheet, and dropped here when the ice melted. Other erratics in the Hadrian's Wall area include grey-green volcanic rocks from the Lake District, sandstone and limestone boulders from Cumbria and more rarely, granite from Shap Fell.

In the nick

As you drive or walk along the line of Hadrian's Wall look out for distinctive 'nicks' in the Whin Sill, such as at Sycamore Gap (above). These are meltwater channels, carved by vast amounts of meltwater flowing beneath the ice sheets that once covered this area. The erosive power of the meltwaters must have been immense. These 'nicks' are carved out of the hard dolerite of the Whin Sill, often where it was weakened adjacent to faults.

Icy sandpaper

As ice sheets moved, stones and boulders frozen into the base of the ice scraped the bedrock, like a giant sheet of sandpaper. The bedrock was ground down, forming smooth and streamlined features. The whinstone outcrops near Walltown Quarry are examples of rock surfaces smoothed by the passage of ice. Scouring by the ice created basin-shaped hollows, which, after the ice melted, became the water-filled loughs of the Wall country. The easiest of these to see, and most photographed, is Crag Lough, but Broomlee, Greenlee and Grindon loughs also occupy similar ice-scoured basins.

◀ This is the margin of Solheimajökull glacier in southern Iceland. Note the amount of dirt, sand and boulders in this bottom layer of the ice. It is this that the glacier uses to erode the landscape like sandpaper. The boulders seen here may also become erratics, as they melt out of the ice and are deposited on the ground

Where to go

Walltown Quarry [NY670 660]
Several large glacial erratic boulders, of Scottish granite and Lake District rocks, have been gathered together as part of the Hard Rock Trail.

The ice retreats

Around 15 000 years ago, the arctic conditions that had gripped Britain for so long gradually gave way to a milder, wetter climate. The ice sheets retreated northwards, leaving in their wake a scarred and desolate tundra landscape of bare rock with piles of clay, sand and boulders. It was not barren for long. Lichens and mosses followed by the first plants, such as mountain avens, then dwarf shrubs and grasses soon began to colonise the land and turn it green.

▲ At the margin of Virkisjökull in SE Iceland a whole landscape has been formed by the action of meltwater. Here sands and gravels dominate the sediments, which are being washed out of the glacier margin by huge amounts of meltwater. In areas such as this terraces, mounds and hollows are common. Good examples in the Wall district can be seen around Haltwhistle and Gilsland in the Tyne Valley

Debris dumped by ice

As the ice sheets melted and retreated, debris was dumped at the ice margins. This debris of boulders, stones and clay commonly forms smooth, half egg-shaped mounds known as drumlins. Stranded chunks of ice, which broke off from the main ice sheet, would have melted where they lay, forming hollows known as kettle holes such as the one pictured here near Warden.

Living on the edge

Soon after the ice melted Britain's tundra landscapes would have been home to reindeer and elk. No evidence of these animals has been preserved near Hadrian's Wall, but their remains have been found in other parts of northern England. The first human settlers arrived in Northumberland about 10 000 years ago. They were hunter-gatherers, living off deer, fish and edible plants.

Brown bear – probably became extinct in Britain around 1500 years ago

Wolf – survived until relatively recently in Britain, some wolves remained in Scotland until 1700

Northern lynx – may have been present in Britain until the 6th or 7th century, more recently than previously thought

Forests return

The original tundra-like landscape was soon replaced by a covering of low growing trees and shrubs such as birch, aspen and willow. Gradually, other trees such as pine, oak, elm and ash colonized the area until it was completely forested, apart from crags and very wet areas. Alder seemed to be the last tree to reach northern areas and did so by approximately 7000 years ago. Most of the area remained forested until humans began felling trees. Wolf, bear and lynx lived in these woods.

Where to go

Warden [NY909 656]
A fine small kettle hole lies on the west side of the road, immediately north of its junction with the A69.

Vindolanda area [NY778 663]
From near the Long Stone, drumlins are conspicuous in the area west of Vindolanda.

Ice

A lasting legacy

As the ice melted it left behind a moulded landscape. Lakes, some of which persist to the present day, formed in ice-eroded and sediment dammed basins. In other shallower basins peat formed and new habitats began to develop, growing more every year. Specialist plants and animals colonised and important wildlife havens such as the Roman Wall Loughs and Border Mires now exist in the Hadrian's Wall area as a constant reminder of our icy past.

▸ Whooper swan
▸ Teal

▾ Crag Lough

In the mire

Mires (sometimes called bogs) formed in depressions left by the ice sheets. Because of the high rainfall and poor drainage, moisture-loving plants such as sphagnum mosses (top right) grow well. The wet conditions mean that their remains do not break down, but accumulate as peat. This builds up, at approximately a metre every thousand years, and is today over 12 metres deep in places. Removal of trees by early settlers may have aided the formation of mires and bogs, which in some areas may be only five to six thousand years old.

Bogs support unusual plants that can withstand wet conditions and low nitrogen levels. Bog rosemary, cranberry (right), cotton grass and sundews all thrive in such places. The sundew catches insects on its sticky leaves to get its nitrogen. Both round-leaved and greater sundew can be found here. In addition to these plants, specialised insects such as the large heath butterfly make their home on bogs. Northumberland is home to most of England's population of large heath butterflies.

◄ Bog asphodel, cotton grass and cross leaved heath

Loughs

The loughs which are so characteristic of the Wall country, are naturally nutrient poor and support unusual communities of plants within them and around their margins. They are internationally important and designated as Special Areas of Conservation (SACs) under the European Habitats Directive. A variety of wildlife is associated with the loughs. Bird life, particularly wintering wildfowl, includes whooper swan, goldeneye, widgeon and teal. Otters live in and around the loughs, feeding on fish, amphibians and crayfish.

▼ Otter tracks into Greenlee Lough

Where to go

Steel Rigg [NY751 676]
Fine views of Crag Lough with whinstone crags above.

Allolee [NY695 668]
View of mire in a hollow at the base of the Whin Sill ridge.

Bell Crag Flow [NY777 728]
One of the internationally important Border Mires. Mire and peat cuttings are visible from a boardwalk.

Grindon Lough [NY805 675]
Viewed from the Stanegate road this is an excellent place to watch wildfowl, especially with a telescope or binoculars in winter.

Greenlee Lough [NY769 700]
Boardwalk across the mire and fen and bird hide.

The Evolving Landscape

Early settlers

The Romans may have been the first to utilise the area's mineral resources on a large scale, but people had been exploiting and altering the region's landscape for thousands of years before the Romans arrived.

Early evidence

Archaeological studies provide evidence for early settlement in the area. In addition, techniques such as pollen analysis allow us to reconstruct past vegetation cover and discover the effect of human impact upon it. All plants produce pollen, unique to individual plant types. Most pollen is carried by the wind and when it falls on the surface of a steadily accumulating peat bog it becomes incorporated into the peat layers. By coring the peat and sampling it at set intervals, we can recognise changes in the proportion of pollen of different species at particular points in time. A sequence of such cores indicates the varying proportions of particular plants in the local landscape over time. Radiocarbon dating enables us to give precise dates to deposits.

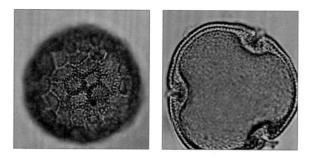

▲ Pollen grains magnified about a thousand times. Note the dramatic differences between these examples of knotgrass (left) and lime (right)

Studies of fossilized pollen from the Hadrian's Wall area reveal that Mesolithic hunter-gatherers lived here around 8000 years ago and created small-scale clearings in the forest. Such evidence has been recorded from pollen at Sells Burn north of Sewingshields. These clearings in the original wildwood forest were probably to aid hunting, as deer and other animals would be attracted to open grassy areas within the dense forest.

▼ Goatstones

First farmers

There is evidence of land clearance, dating from about 3900 BC at Fellend Moss near Walltown. Cereals are known to have been in cultivation by about 1200 BC, towards the end of the Bronze Age.

Debate continues over the changes in vegetation cover during the Iron Age, and during and after the Roman occupation. By the late Iron Age however, when the Romans arrived, the landscape was almost certainly open and extensively cultivated. Forest cover may have returned after the departure of the Romans.

From the Norman period until the 16th century the Fellend Moss area seems to have been less densely settled than previously. A final clearance phase is dated to c. AD1516, and this continued, without interruption, up until the present day. Only recently has tree cover started to increase with the instigation of planting regimes.

▶ The Mare and Foal south of Caw Gap. This monument may have consisted of at least four stones

First builders

Early humans exploited the geology of the surrounding land. Standing stones such as the Mare and Foal and the Goatstones are testimony to this.

We are unsure exactly when these stones were erected and for what purpose, but it is thought they probably date from the Bronze Age, around 4000 years ago. It is possible that they may have been associated with burials or were part of larger monuments.

Where to go

Mare and Foal [NY725 663]
These sandstones provide evidence for human activity in the area in the second millennium BC.

Goatstones [NY829 747]
Four stones standing on open ground near to Ravenshaugh Crags with extensive views in all directions. The top of the easternmost stone is covered in cupmarks.

Greenlee Lough [NY777 697]
There is a circle of stones on a south facing rocky slope overlooking the southern shore of Greenlee Lough. There are at least fourteen stones in the circle, four of which are large sandstone boulders.

The Evolving Landscape

Up to the present

As we have seen, colliding continents, tropical seas and kilometre-thick ice sheets have all played their part in shaping the area, but the landscape continues to evolve. Agriculture and forestry have altered the landscape on a large scale and conservation work continues to improve the diversity of the wildlife.

Tree-mendous!

Woodlands provide homes and food for a multitude of organisms including fungi, lichens and higher plants, together with animals and birds, such as red squirrels, bats and spotted flycatchers. Areas of new native woodland have recently been planted in the Northumberland National Park. These woods contain broad-leaved species such as oak, birch, rowan, alder and willow, and link with existing woodlands, helping wildlife to spread. This increase in native tree cover is the first seen since the trees began to be cleared in Mesolithic times.

▼ New native woodland planting adjacent to Greenlee Lough

THE TEASDALE WOOD

Bogged down

Large conifer forests were planted after World War II in an attempt to make Britain self sufficient in timber. Areas of agricultural land that had not had trees since Mesolithic times were planted with fast growing non-native softwood trees such as sitka spruce and lodgepole pine. Much wet land was drained, including areas of peat bogs. Over wide areas, the natural vegetation was replaced with huge forests such as those developed at Wark and Kielder. A recognition of the conservation value of peat bogs, has encouraged the clearance of trees from mires (right), to restore these important habitats.

Farming

Sheep farming has been a major factor in changing the landscape. As native woodlands were cleared, grazing prevented tree regeneration and destroyed much heather moorland. In addition, the practice of liming and the application of inorganic fertilizers produced 'improved' fields with more palatable grasses. The system of agricultural subsidies operating since the 1950s has contributed to overgrazing, though in recent years sheep levels have been reduced and a variety of stewardship and environmental schemes have improved heather cover and protected mires.

The ongoing story

The Earth processes that have shaped the area over millions of years continue today. The hills are being eroded as rapidly as at many times in the geological past. Rivers are removing the wasting material and dumping it on their flanks as spreads of alluvium, especially during periodic floods.

The fold-out geological map

Areas of alluvium show up prominently on the geological fold-out map.

Floods and the future

The previous chapters have shown how the climate has changed over millions of years. The changes continue today. If global warming causes average temperatures to rise, will we see different plants and animals? There is already evidence that some invertebrates such as the comma butterfly are moving northwards. Will it still be wet enough for peat bogs to continue growing? These are questions that we can't answer, but it is certain that the landscape will continue to evolve as it has over the hundreds of millions of years of Earth history recorded in the rocks and landscape of the Hadrian's Wall area.

Where to go

Stonefolds [NY772 701]
New tree planting may be seen adjacent to Greenlee Lough.

Irthing Gorge [NY638 679]
The fine wooded valley is a Woodland Trust site.

Bell Crag Flow [NY777 727]
A boardwalk gives access to a bog in the forest where restoration has taken place. There are also old peat cuttings.

Useful information and further reading

We hope you have enjoyed reading about why the Hadrian's Wall landscape is such a special place, and some of the ways its rocks and landscape have influenced its history over many centuries. Within a short book of this sort it has obviously been possible only to touch briefly upon a selection of topics, but we hope that we have whetted your appetite to find out more about this fascinating area. Much more detail on many topics can be found in a variety of publications, a selection of which is listed here. This is by no means an exhaustive list, but includes some of the most important and better-known texts. References to even more detailed sources of information will be found in many of these.

DUNHAM, K.C. 1990. Geology of the Northern Pennine Orefield Volume 1 Tyne to Stainmore. *Memoir of the British Geological Survey. Second Edition.* ISBN 0 11 884471 7. An important classic work of British geological literature describing in detail the geology of the mining areas of the Northern Pennines with descriptions of the minerals, the mineral deposits and with detailed descriptions of the mines and their history.

FRODSHAM, P. 2004. *Archaeology in Northumberland National Park.* CBA Research Report 136. Council for British Archaeology 2004. ISBN 1-902771-38-9. A volume containing an overview of the Park's history and archaeology and the impact of humans on the landscape. Also contains case studies and new original research.

FROST, D.V. and HOLLIDAY, D.W. 1980. Geology of the Country around Bellingham. *Memoir of the Geological Survey of Great Britain.* ISBN 0 11 8841378. A detailed description of the geology of the area between Hadrian's Wall and Bellingham.

HARLEY, S. 1999. *In the Bewick Vein: The story of a Northumberland Lead Mine.* Honeycrook Press, Haydon Bridge, Northumberland ISBN 0 9534512 0 8. A very readable historical account of this important old mine.

JOHNSON, G.A.L. (editor) 1995. *Robson's Geology of North East England.* Transactions of the Natural History Society of Northumbria. Vol. 56, Part 5. ISSN 0144-221X. A comprehensive description of the geology of the whole of North East England.

JOHNSON, G.A.L. 1997. *Geology of Hadrian's Wall.* Geologists' Association Guide No. 59. ISBN 0-900717-49-1. A field guide which relates the local geology to the Wall and its related archaeological structures.

LUNN, A. 2004. *Northumberland with Alston Moor.* Harper Collins, London. ISBN 000 718484 0 (Hardback); 000 718483 2 (Paperback). A guide to the area's natural history, including some geology.

PARKER, J. undated. *Haltwhistle and Beyond.* TUPS Books, Newcastle upon Tyne. ISBN 1 901237 24 9. A local history of the Haltwhistle area which includes information on quarrying and coal mining.

SCRUTTON, C.T. (editor) second edition 2004. *Northumbrian Rocks and Landscape.* Yorkshire Geological Society. ISBN 0-9501656-4-6. A series of guided geological walks through parts of North East England, including parts of the Hadrian's Wall area.

Geological Maps

The following 1:50 000 scale British Geological Survey maps cover the area described in this book:

Bewcastle . . . . (12)
Bellingham . . . . (13)
Morpeth . . . . (14)
Brampton . . . . (18)
Hexham . . . . (19)
Newcastle upon Tyne . . . . (20)

Details of all British Geological Survey publications may be obtained from:

British Geological Survey
Kingsley Dunham Centre
Keyworth
Nottingham
NG12 5GG
Tel: 0115 936 3241
E-mail: sales@bgs.ac.uk

Acknowledgements

This book has been prepared by the British Geological Survey and Northumberland National Park Authority with funding from the Sustainable Land-Won and Marine Dredged Aggregate Minerals Programme (SAMP). SAMP is funded through the Department for Environment, Food and Rural Affairs as part of the Aggregate Levy Sustainability Fund (ALSF), administered by the Mineral Industry Research Organisation for the Office of the Deputy Prime Minister. This publication and references within it to any methodology, process, service, manufacturer, or company do not constitute its endorsement or recommendation by the Department for Environment, Food and Rural Affairs, The Office of the Deputy Prime Minister or the Minerals Industry Research Organisation.

The authors would like to thank many people and organisations for providing information and constructive comment and for permission to use individual photographs and illustrations. Acknowledgement for individual images from sources outside BGS and NNPA is provided below. We thank colleagues for comments and suggestions and for the use of photographs, in particular Derek Proudlock and Albert Weir within the NNPA and Sarah Arkley within BGS.

We would like to acknowledge the input of Jonathan Larwood, Claire Furness and Mike Sutcliffe at English Nature, staff at the Northumberland Wildlife Trust and the co-operation of landowners and quarry operators. In particular we are grateful for the courtesy and assistance afforded by the National Trust, whose Hadrian's Wall estate extends from Cawfields Quarry to Housesteads, and for help provided by staff at English Heritage. Thanks also to Janet Simkin for photographs and information about lichens, to Robin Birley of the Vindolanda Trust for advice on the Vindolanda Tablets and to Gill Lawrence for photographs for use as textural backgrounds. Hand-painted illustrations are by Elizabeth Pickett.

Design:
Infinite Design, Newcastle upon Tyne. www.infinitedesign.com
Linda H. Carroll (Northumberland National Park)

Printed in England by Printers (Coast) Limited, Newcastle upon Tyne
Printed on environmentally-friendly paper

BGS © NERC, 2006

Satellite Image of the Hadrian's Wall Area

This satellite image was taken by the LANDSAT 5 Thematic Sensor under near–cloudless conditions. It is a false colour composite of three infrared frequencies displayed as varying strengths of red, green and blue. Urban areas appear in shades of dark-blue and grey, vegetated farmland appears in shades of brown, whilst soil, bare rock and open moorland appear in shades of green. The image was taken on a winter's morning with the sun in the southeast and low in the sky. Topographical features cause shadows in their lee that make interpretation easier. Compare this satellite image with the geological map.

Note how the strong ridges formed by the Whin Sill (with Hadrian's Wall on top) and some of the limestones and sandstones stand out well in the image. Note also how the flat, fertile flood plain of the River South Tyne stands out as a featureless strip of brown and green either side of the river.

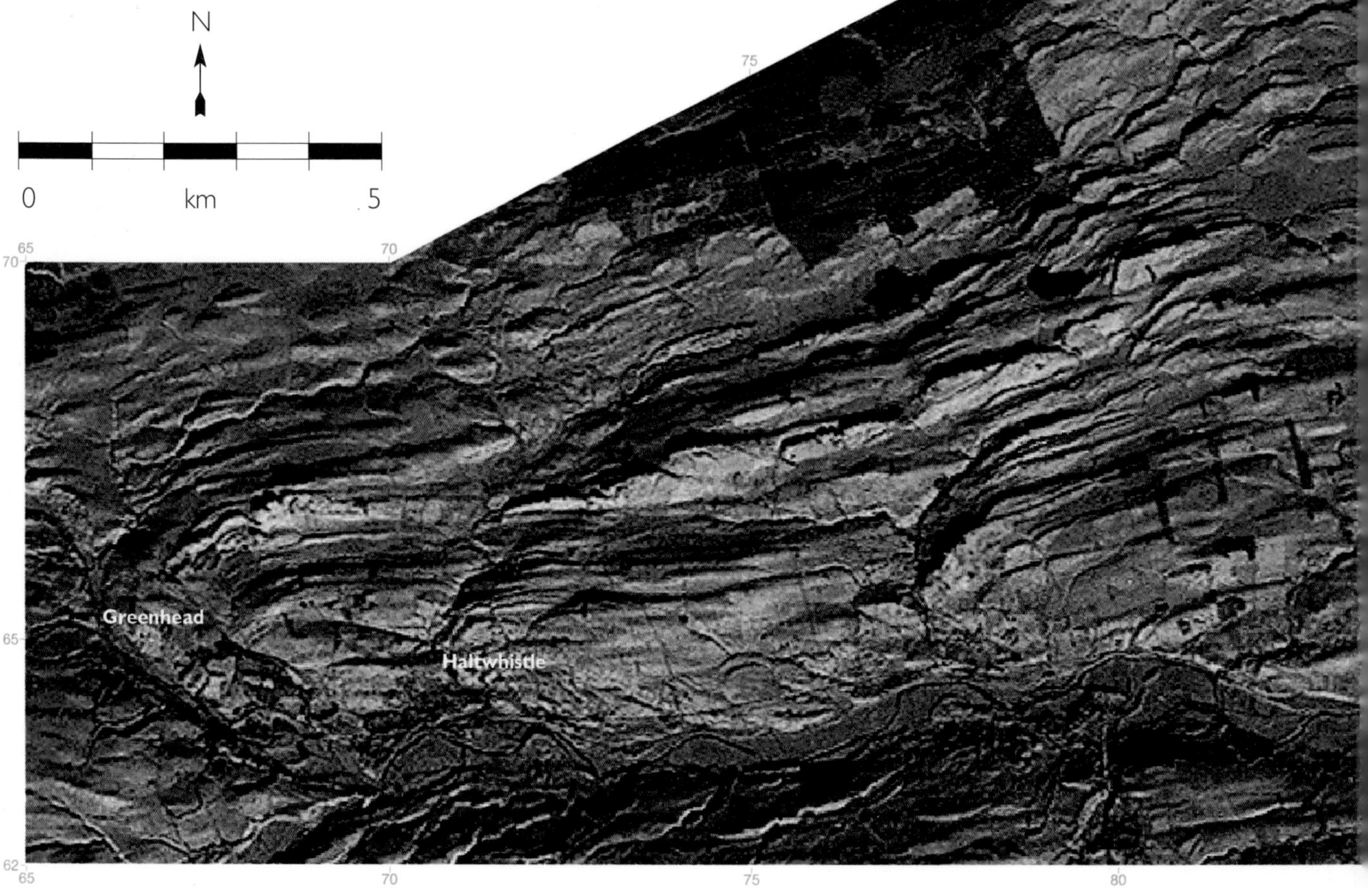

N

0   km   5

Greenhead

Haltwhistle